The Christmas Nativity Tale

Licensed exclusively to Top That Publishing Ltd
Tide Mill Way, Woodbridge, Suffolk, IP12 1AP, UK
www.topthatpublishing.com
Copyright © 2016 Tide Mill Media
All rights reserved
0 2 4 6 8 9 7 5 3 1
Manufactured in China

Long, long ago, in a town called Nazareth, a woman called Mary was visited by an angel. The angel told Mary that she had been chosen to have a very special baby – the son of God. 'You will call him Jesus,' the angel said.

Later that year, the Emperor announced that there would be a census and everyone in the land must return to their place of birth, to be counted.
So Mary and her husband Joseph had to travel from Nazareth to Bethlehem.

The journey was very long and tiring and Mary was going to have her baby very soon. Mary travelled most of the journey on a donkey, led by Joseph.

Far away, three wise men were studying the night sky when they spotted a new, bright star. They had been waiting a long time for this sign, as it meant that a very special baby was going to be born.

So, the wise men set out on a great journey to follow the star.

When Mary and Joseph arrived in Bethlehem, they looked for somewhere to stay, but at every inn the story was the same. 'I'm sorry, there's no more room!' the innkeepers said. Everyone had returned to be counted, so the town was full.

Finally, at the very last inn in town, the kind innkeeper
offered Mary and Joseph the only space he had left,
in his stable, with the animals.

That night, in the cosy stable, Mary gave birth to baby Jesus. There was no cradle in the stable, so Mary and Joseph wrapped him in a blanket and put him in a manger full of straw.

On a faraway hillside, three shepherds were
looking after their sheep. Suddenly, a burst
of light filled the sky and an angel
appeared, telling them that a very
special baby had been born, and
that he was the son of God.
So the shepherds went
to Bethlehem to see him.

The three wise men arrived at the stable after the shepherds. When they saw Jesus, they knew that he would be a leader of men, the King of Kings. They gave him gifts of gold, frankincense and myrrh, and knelt to worship him.

Everyone was overjoyed at the birth of Jesus.
When the shepherds went on their way, they spread
the wonderful news about this very special baby –
the son of God and the saviour of the world.